THE BAKER STREET
IRREGULARS

THE ADVENTURE OF THE
CHARGE OF THE OLD BRIGADE

TONY LEE and DAN BOULTWOOD

EDGE
FRANKLIN
WATTS

LONDON·SYDNEY

First published in 2011 by
Franklin Watts
338 Euston Road
London NW1 3BH

Franklin Watts Australia
Level 17/207 Kent Street
Sydney, NSW 2000

Special thanks to Leslie S. Klinger for his invaluable contribution to this series

A CIP catalogue record for this book
is available from the British Library

ISBN: 978 1 4451 0344 0

3 5 7 9 10 8 6 4 2

Printed in China

Franklin Watts is a division of Hachette Children's Books,
an Hachette UK company
www.hachette.co.uk

THE ADVENTURE OF THE
CHARGE OF THE OLD BRIGADE

The story so far...

Sherlock Holmes is *missing,* believed *dead* and
London has fallen into *lawlessness.*

Only the *Baker Street Irregulars,* led by Holmes's protégé
Wiggins are there to help the common people. Aided by
Doctor John Watson and the enigmatic Irene Adler,
the Irregulars will solve *any* crime, *any* mystery.

But the villain of their last adventure, the mysterious *'M'*
is still out there... He's been stopped *twice* now, will they
get a *third* chance to unmask him...?

Wiggins Eliza Pockets

Chen Ash Tiny

The *Crimean War* was a *terrible* one. And our cavalry unit was smack bang in the middle of it.

They were *tough* times. We were tired and always hungry – we lived off what we could find. *Brothers,* bound together by a need for survival.

"We survived on what we *looted.* Nobody expected the hoard we found that day."

"A king's ransom in gold and jewels."

"We knew that if declared, it would become the property of the *King.* We had to hide it."

"The plan was to wait a year from the end of the war and then collect it."

But there was a *problem* with this plan.

With the money involved, we were no longer brothers. We were now *rivals* – and not one of us trusted another of the group to hide the gold.

"It was Bob who came up with the new plan. To ask the *Colonel* to arrange it."

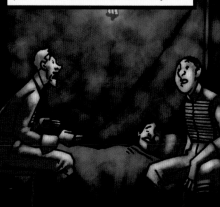

"He was dying of the *sickness* you see. He only had a matter of *weeks* to live."

The London docks.

That barber said that *Archie Lumm* lived at the end of this terrace with his son and granddaughter --

Look! We're just in time!

Help!

Will you *shut up!* You're causing a *terrible racket!*

Help!

I think that's the point!

Crack!

Hey! Get *off* her!

WHAMM!

They took Eliza! They took Nancy!

What? Who did? Where?

I thought they would. That should give us an advantage.

You knew? You let Eliza and Nancy go out to get caught?

And this doesn't bother you? They're just girls! You're as cold as Holmes ever was!

She's not 'just a girl'. Eliza is an Irregular - and don't you forget it.

Pockets, are you ready for this?

As much as anyone could be wearing one of these.

I don't understand! Why is Pockets in a dress?

Once captured, she'll be brought to Eliza, Nancy and Lucy.

From there, she'll help them to escape while we go to visit Windibank.

But why would they capture her?

Because we have a plan.

Excuse me - but I was asked to come here?

My name's Mitchell. Bob Mitchell.

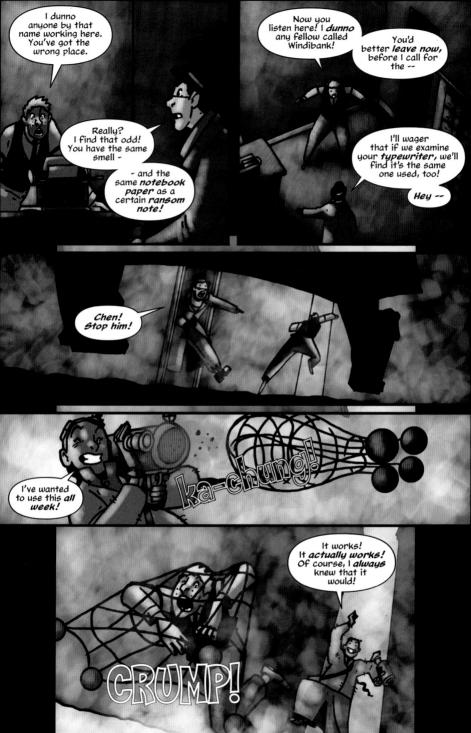

Bradshaw House Stables.

The time has passed on *that* arrangement, Tim! We have discovered that a *master criminal* is involved!

Someone who has *no care* for your family's safety, even if he *gets* the papers!

Why is he here? I said *no police!*

Wiggins! Tiny! What the devil is going on?

Ah. Lord Bradshaw? Inspector Lestrade, *Scotland Yard.* Where's *James Windibank?*

Tell us now and receive a lighter sentence for your role in this *kidnap!*

What? You think I'm *involved?* How could you? These men are my *friends!*

So you *deny* that James Windibank has been *working* for you? You *deny* that you know *'M'?*

If Nancy is harmed - I'll hold you *personally responsible* for it!

James who? I'm sorry - I have *no idea* what you're talking about!

I think he's *telling the truth*, you know!

Lord Bradshaw - does the name *Hosmer Angel* mean anything? That was one of Windibank's many *aliases.*

Yes - yes it *does.* Oh no. Do you mean that *he is the kidnapper?*

It really *is* all my fault, then!

I think that I need to sit down!

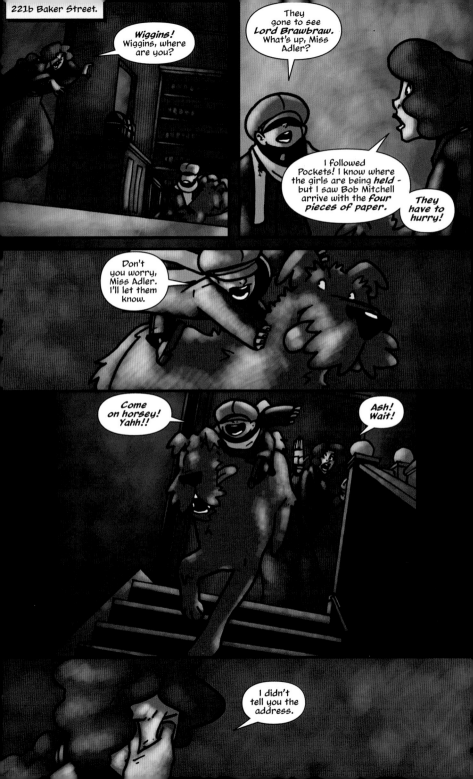

But where does Windibank fit into this? Or 'M'?

What about that name - *O'Reilly* - that we found?

O'Reilly? *Frank* O'Reilly? He was on our *lists!* Came here about five years ago.

He was one of the soldiers that Angel - I mean *Windibank* - was interested in. They spent *hours* talking together.

O'Reilly? So he *is* alive!

And he lives here?

Not any more. Windibank provided him with *money* - an *inheritance*, he said -

- O'Reilly moved out a couple of weeks before 'Hosman Angel' left.

So Windibank comes in, finds one of the men who knew about the gold - and then *spirits him away.*

That *has* to be connected to the *missing girls!* If only we knew where he lived.

But we do. Windibank may have stolen the *address book* - but I have the *original notes.*

Frank O'Reilly lives in *Putney* - less than *two miles* from here.

Putney, London.

Inspector **Lestrade!** I'm so glad you came.

Yes, well it made a nice change from being summoned by a boy on a **dog.**

Is this the right address?

Yes - but the carriage is **gone.** I fear that we may be **too late.**

Frank O'Reilly! James Windibank! Show yourselves!

CRASH!

Mmmph!

Where are they? The girls?

Taken! Two **escaped** - but they were found again.

They've all been taken to where the **gold** is - and when they're of no use, **they'll be killed!**

THE BAKER STREET IRREGULARS

THE ADVENTURE OF THE

FAMILY REUNION

TONY LEE and DAN BOULTWOOD

EDGE